for the
CEM

GW00685277

11+
COMPREHENSION

ges 10–11

ractice

Series editor Tracey Phelps,
the 11+ tutor with a

96% PASS RATE

Published in the UK by Scholastic, 2020

Book End, Range Road, Witney, Oxfordshire, OX29 0YD

Scholastic Ireland, 89E Lagan Road, Dublin Industrial Estate, Glasnevin, Dublin, D11 HP5F

www.scholastic.co.uk

2 3 4 5 6 7 8 9   1 2 3 4 5 6 7 8 9 0

A CIP catalogue record for this book is available from the British Library.

ISBN 978-1407-18376-3

Printed in Great Britain by Bell and Bain Ltd, Glasgow

Paper made from wood grown in sustainable forests and other controlled sources.

Author

Tracey Phelps

Editorial team

Rachel Morgan, Suzanne Holloway, Audrey Stokes, Vicki Yates

Sarah Davies, Julia Roberts

Design team

Dipa Mistry, Andrea Lewis

Acknowledgements

p49 *Prometheus the Fire-Giver* extract from Scholastic Short Reads Box 4 © Scholastic Ltd; p52 *The Pied Piper of Hamelin* extract from Scholastic Short Reads Box 5 © Scholastic Ltd; p57 *My Father's War* extract from Scholastic Short Reads Box 5 © Scholastic Ltd

Contents

About the CEM Test

About the CEM test

The Centre for Evaluation and Monitoring (CEM) is one of the leading providers of the tests that grammar schools use in selecting students at 11+. The CEM test assesses a student's ability in Verbal Reasoning, Non-verbal Reasoning, English and Mathematics. Pupils typically take the CEM test at the start of Year 6.

Students answer multiple-choice questions and record their answers on a separate answer sheet. This answer sheet is then marked via OMR (Optical Mark Recognition) scanning technology.

The content and question type may vary slightly each year. The English and Verbal Reasoning components have included synonyms, antonyms, word associations, shuffled sentences, cloze (gap fill) passages and comprehension questions.

The Mathematics and Non-verbal Reasoning components span the Key Stage 2 Mathematics curriculum, with emphasis on **worded problems**. It is useful to note that the CEM test does include mathematics topics introduced at Year 6, such as ratio, proportion and probability.

The other main provider of such tests is GL Assessment. The GLA test assesses the same subjects as the CEM test and uses a multiple-choice format.

About this book

Scholastic 11+ Comprehension for the CEM Test is part of the Pass Your 11+ series and offers authentic multiple-choice comprehension activities.

This book offers:

- Challenging comprehension questions covering fiction and non-fiction.

- Targeted practice and opportunities for children to test their understanding and develop their comprehension skills.

- Opportunities for children to sharpen skills such as inference and deduction, which are an essential part of the CEM test

- Short answers at the end of the book.

- Short answers at the end of the book.

- Extended answers online with useful explanations at **www.scholastic.co.uk/pass-your-11-plus/extras** or via the QR code opposite.

Comprehension 1

The Tower of London

The Tower of London remains the most perfectly preserved fortress in Britain. It was first constructed during the reign of William I and added to by successive monarchs. The Tower has served as a palace, a place of execution and a prison. It has also housed the Royal Mint, where the nation's coins were manufactured. Thirty-seven Yeoman Warders – commonly known as Beefeaters – act as guards and the
5   Tower is their permanent home all year round.

The Tower of London houses the priceless Crown Jewels which are used in coronations and other grand state occasions. They comprise crowns, sceptres, orbs and swords and were first created in 1661, when Charles II was crowned. The original medieval jewels – which dated from the time of Edward the Confessor – were all destroyed after the execution of Charles I in 1649. Coronation ceremonies of a new
10   king or queen are steeped in history and begin with him or her proceeding to Westminster Abbey to be anointed with holy oil. They are then invested with royal robes and the Royal Sword. Then, the Crown of St Edward is placed on the new sovereign's head, trumpets begin to sound and guns at the Tower are fired and heard all over London. The last coronation was that of Queen Elizabeth II, in 1953.

One of the Tower's darkest mysteries concerns two boy princes – the sons and heirs of Edward IV –
15   Edward and Richard. The king died suddenly in 1483 and his son Edward came to London to be prepared to be crowned. His ambitious uncle, Richard of Gloucester, met Edward and had him lodged at the Tower. He then persuaded the queen to allow her younger son to be sent to the Tower as company for Edward. However, during the ensuing summer, the young princes were seen less and less until one day they simply vanished and were never seen again. Uncle Richard became Richard III later that same year. Much later, in
20   1674, when Charles II was king, two skeletons were found hidden under the staircase leading into St John's Chapel in the Tower of London. At the time, it was widely believed that their uncle had them murdered.

The exchange of exotic animals was customary between medieval monarchs and, upon receipt of three lions as a gift from Holy Roman Emperor Frederick II in the year 1235, King Henry III established a Royal Menagerie at the Tower. In 1252, a polar bear arrived as a gift from the King of Norway. Tigers, monkeys,
25   elephants, snakes and even alligators followed and the menagerie proved to be a hugely popular attraction. Ultimately, however, the workers at the Tower lacked the skills to be able to control the animals properly and appreciate how dangerous they were. In 1821, after yet another attack on a staff member – who was mauled and then killed by a lion – the Duke of Wellington ordered that the menagerie be closed. The animals were all taken to The Regent's Park which became the location of the present London Zoo.

30   An 'unkindness' of ravens are the traditional guardians of the Tower of London. Legend has it that should the ravens ever leave, the White Tower would crumble and a great disaster would befall England. There is a Raven Master who knows each bird by name – they are called Hardey, Thor, Odin, Gwyllum, Cedric, Hugine and Munin – and who feeds them raw meat twice a day, plus bird biscuits soaked in blood and the occasional rat. To prevent the ravens from flying away, they have part of their wings clipped on the right
35   side. This procedure does not hurt the birds, but just unbalances their flight and ensures that they stay safe and don't stray too far from the Tower. The ravens are very clever and they will happily play together and steal and hoard shiny objects like pieces of metal and small stones to impress each other.

Carefully read through the passage on the previous page and circle the correct answers below.

1 What is the nickname of the warders who guard the Tower of London?

A. Raven Masters

B. Beefeaters

C. Mudlarks

D. Costermongers

2 In which year were the Crown Jewels made?

A. 1649

B. 1625

C. 1661

D. 1483

3 Which monarch did Richard of Gloucester become?

A. Richard I

B. Richard the Lionheart

C. Richard III

D. Richard II

4 How did Henry III come to own a great white bear?

A. He brought it back with him from a royal visit to Iceland.

B. He was gifted it by another king.

C. He rented it from London Zoo.

D. His wife, the queen, bought it for him as a gift.

/4

5 How many years after the young princes' disappearance were the two skeletons found?

A. About 190 years

B. About 290 years

C. About 240 years

D. About 170 years

---

6 What makes the ravens' biscuits moist?

A. They are dipped in milk.

B. They are coated with olive oil.

C. They are dipped in the finest Ceylon tea.

D. They are soaked in blood.

---

7 What relation was the young Prince Edward to Richard of Gloucester?

A. He was his uncle.

B. He was his nephew.

C. He was his brother.

D. He was his cousin.

---

8 How does the Raven Master make certain that his birds don't fly far away from the Tower?

A. He ties heavy weights to their feet so they can't take off.

B. He keeps them locked up in a large cage.

C. He straps their wings together so that they can't fly.

D. He has their wings trimmed on one side so that it makes it difficult for them to fly.

/4

9 Which of the following statements is true?

Option 1   More than three dozen Yeoman Warders guard the Tower of London.

Option 2   Henry VIII established the Royal Menagerie when he acquired three lions.

Option 3   Royal coronations traditionally take place at Buckingham Palace.

Option 4   The skeletons were discovered in one of the chapels in the Tower.

A. Option 1 only

B. Options 2 and 3

C. Options 2, 3 and 4

D. Options 1, 2, and 4

---

10 Which of the following statements is not true?

Option 1   Charles I was beheaded in 1661.

Option 2   There are six ravens who guard the Tower.

Option 3   Coins were once made in the Tower of London at the Royal Mint.

Option 4   Edward IV's death was sudden and unexpected.

A. Option 1 only

B. Options 1 and 2

C. Options 1 and 3

D. Options 3 and 4

---

11 What is the collective noun for a group of ravens?

A. An unkindness

B. A colony

C. A group

D. A parliament

/3

12 Why was the Royal Menagerie closed?

A. The animals became too expensive to keep.

B. The queen needed extra space to accommodate her racehorses.

C. There was an outbreak of rabies.

D. The animals were too dangerous and kept attacking people.

---

13 How much are the Crown Jewels worth?

A. In excess of £3 billion

B. Approximately one million pounds

C. They are priceless.

D. It is a closely guarded secret and only the queen knows the value of the jewels.

---

14 Under whose reign was the first set of crown jewels created?

A. Charles II

B. Edward the Confessor

C. Henry III

D. William I

---

15 Where in the city was London's first zoo located?

A. Green Park

B. The Royal Botanical Gardens at Kew

C. The Regent's Park

D. Hampstead Heath

/4

Comprehension 2

Nellie Bly

Nellie Bly was born in America in 1864. She was the third youngest and 13th child of Michael and Mary Cochran and from an early age was fiercely ambitious; her goal was to become a teacher at a time when it was most unusual for women to pursue a career.

In 1885, Nellie read an article in the *Pittsburgh Dispatch* newspaper that criticised women for aspiring to
5 gain an education and forge a career. Nellie was so incensed by the piece that she communicated her wrath in a letter to the editor, George Madden. Madden was so impressed with the letter that he offered Bly a job as a journalist. By 1887, Nellie had established herself as a pioneer in the field of investigative journalism and had written several influential articles which had led to a wave of reforms to women's rights. By 1888, Bly was a senior journalist at the powerful newspaper the *New York World*.

10 In 1889, after reading *Around the World in Eighty Days* – by Jules Verne – Nellie was inspired to attempt the very same feat and try to beat the time taken by the book's central character, Phileas Fogg. Nellie approached her editor at the newspaper, John Cockerill, who swiftly agreed to sponsor Nellie's ambitious venture. She meticulously planned her route and decided to travel west to east, boarding the steamer *Augusta Victoria* on 14 November 1889, bound for England. Upon her arrival in Southampton, Bly was met by the *New York*
15 *World's* London correspondent, who had exciting news: Jules Verne himself had heard of Nellie's quest and wanted to meet her in France. This was a bitter-sweet development for Nellie; it would be an honour to meet the author, but it would mean that she would have to deviate from her route and forsake precious time. Nellie dined with Verne at his home and then set off to catch a train to connect her to a steamer sailing to Ceylon – now Sri Lanka – arriving on 8 December 1889. Nellie then boarded the *Oriental* for the 3500-mile crossing
20 to Hong Kong. En route, the ship stopped in Singapore to refuel and it was here that the intrepid journalist acquired a travelling companion: a fez-wearing miniature monkey whom she named McGinty. During the crossing, Nellie had to endure a violent cyclone storm and then some most unwelcome news when she arrived: she learned that a rival publication, The *Cosmopolitan*, had sent one of their best journalists, Elizabeth Bisland, to try to beat Bly's time. Bisland had left America within six hours of Bly setting out and
25 was travelling east to west.

The world was gripped by the contest and newspapers reported daily on the race between the two women. Upon her arrival in Hong Kong – on 25 December 1889 – Bly was dismayed to learn that Bisland had passed through the British colony several days earlier. Undeterred, Nellie pressed on and set sail on 7 January 1890 for San Francisco, arriving back on American soil a fortnight later – a whole day ahead of
30 schedule. Bly was delighted, but her mood soon changed; heavy snowstorms had resulted in public train services being cancelled and she still had a 2500-mile train journey to make it to the finish line in New York.

However, unbeknown to Bly, her rival's luck had also just run out. Back in England, Bisland was frustrated to learn that the high-speed German steamer *Ems*, due to take her from Southampton to New York, had been cancelled. She was forced to divert to Ireland and board the much slower ship, the *Bothnia*.

35 Meanwhile, the *New York World's* owner, Joseph Pulitzer, sent a private train to bring Nellie home to New York and she finally arrived to the applause of thousands of well-wishers on 25 January 1890, at 3.51pm – 72 days, 6 hours, 11 minutes and 14 seconds after leaving. Bly had bettered Phileas Fogg's fictional journey time by over seven days. Elizabeth Bisland arrived five days later.

Carefully read through the passage on the previous page and circle the correct answers below.

1 How many siblings did Nellie Bly have?

A. Thirteen

B. Eleven

C. Fourteen

D. Fifteen

---

2 What was the name of the first newspaper that Nellie worked for?

A. The *New York World*

B. The *Pennsylvania Herald*

C. The *Pittsburgh Dispatch*

D. *Around the World in Eighty Days*

---

3 Who met Nellie when she first disembarked from the *Augusta Victoria* in England?

A. The London correspondent of the newspaper that Nellie worked for

B. Jules Verne's representative in England

C. Jules Verne

D. Elizabeth Bisland

---

4 Which of the following statements is <u>not</u> true?

A. Nellie felt privileged to have been invited to meet Jules Verne.

B. Nellie was anxious not to waste any time during her world record attempt.

C. Nellie was inspired by the novel *Around the World in Eighty Days*.

D. Nellie's epic journey took her around the world from east to west.

/4

5 What kind of human clothing did Nellie's miniature monkey favour?

A. A miniature coat

B. A little hat

C. A small waistcoat

D. A tiny scarf

---

6 Why did the *Oriental* stop in Singapore?

A. To allow some passengers to disembark

B. To pick up extra crew

C. To take on extra fuel

D. To replenish food supplies

---

7 On which sea crossing did Nellie experience a violent cyclone?

A. America to England

B. Sri Lanka to Hong Kong

C. France to Ceylon

D. Hong Kong to San Francisco

---

8 For which publication did Nellie's rival adventurer work?

A. The *New York World*

B. The *Hong Kong Morning Post*

C. The *Pittsburgh Dispatch*

D. The *Cosmopolitan*

/4

9 Which of the following statements is not true?

Option 1   Nellie Bly was working as a journalist at the time of her 18th birthday.

Option 2   Bly and Bisland set off on their record attempts at exactly the same time.

Option 3   Nellie travelled by rail to board the ship that would take her to Ceylon.

Option 4   Nellie Bly originally aspired to follow a career in teaching.

A. Options 1 and 2

B. Options 2 and 3

C. Options 1 and 4

D. Options 1, 2, 3 and 4

10 Which of the following statements is true?

Option 1   Nellie Bly arrived back in America on 21 January 1890.

Option 2   Nellie Bly was a staunch advocate for women's rights.

Option 3   George Madden was the editor of the *New York World*.

Option 4   Elizabeth Bisland arrived back in New York on 30 January 1890.

A. Options 1, 2 and 4

B. Options 1 and 3

C. Options 2 and 4

D. Option 2 only

11 What type of state was Hong Kong in 1889?

A. An independent country

B. A British colony

C. A French colony

D. A Chinese province

/3

12 From which country did Elizabeth Bisland eventually sail back to America?

A. Germany

B. England

C. Ireland

D. Iceland

---

13 Which of the following statements is not true?

A. Nellie's rival, Elizabeth Bisland, left New York in November 1889.

B. Nellie sailed from Sri Lanka on the *Oriental*.

C. Jules Verne resided in France.

D. Nellie was furious when she read a critical article in the *New York World*.

---

14 Where in the world did Nellie celebrate Christmas 1889?

A. Hong Kong

B. Singapore

C. England

D. Sri Lanka

---

15 What was the name of Jules Verne's fictional world-circumnavigator?

A. John Cockerill

B. McGinty

C. Joseph Pulitzer

D. Phileas Fogg

/4

Comprehension 3

The Cotswolds

The Cotswolds are a range of limestone hills running over in a north-easterly direction from Bath. There are hundreds of villages in the area that are made entirely out of Cotswold stone, making them very attractive and popular with tourists. At one time, there were dozens of quarries mining the stone; Taynton quarry, near Burford, was the source of the stone used in the building of the Oxford University colleges. Due to the strict building regulations in a conservation area, there are still a good number of quarries in the region, extracting the stone for repairs and for the construction of stone walls and new buildings.

A charming small town, Burford is a mere 20 miles west of Oxford. The town is home to many individual shops and also the oldest pharmacy in England – Reavley's – which dates back to 1734.

Burford is hugely popular with visitors for its beauty, history and shopping, especially antiques.

During the English Civil War, there was a group of activists known as Levellers who challenged the authority of Parliament and it was in 1649 the town of Burford that they were rounded up and imprisoned by Cromwell. Three of them were executed in the churchyard and the bullet holes from that siege can still be seen to this day.

On the Saturday closest to 18 May every year, this event is marked by celebrating 'Levellers' Day' with a carnival.

Bourton-on-the-Water is known as the Venice of the Cotswolds because of the five bridges crossing over the River Windrush that flows through its centre. It is also the most visited village of the Cotswolds, as there are many attractions to see.

The queen of crime, author Agatha Christie, is said to have stayed at the Mousetrap Inn in Bourton while writing her successful stage play of the same name in 1952. The play has since become the longest running stage play ever and is still being performed at St Martin's Theatre in London's West End to this day.

Bourton's Cotswold Perfumery has made personalised fragrances for Her Majesty Queen Elizabeth II.

The pretty town of Nailsworth nestles in a wooded valley to the east of Stroud and is renowned for its selection of award-winning restaurants, pubs and cafes. *The Sunday Times* recently listed Nailsworth as one of the top ten most desirable places to live in Britain.

One of the town's delightful quirks is its town crier, who loudly announces events such as the ever-popular, bustling monthly farmers' market and Nailsworth Festival of Arts each May. The town dates back to the 12th century and much of its prosperity stems from the mills that line its rivers. Many have since been converted to hotels or flats.

Right at the top of Nailsworth is New Lawn, home of the town's football club, Forest Green Rovers. Founded in 1889, the club reached new heights in 2017 by winning promotion to the English Football League for the first time in their history.

Nearby is the reputedly haunted Woodchester Mansion.

Centred around the 15th-century Market Place, Northleach is a thriving Cotswold town and it is also the smallest town in England. It is said that a secret maze of stone-vaulted tunnels runs beneath the houses and streets of Northleach. Whether this was the result of mining or some more obscure activity remains unknown.

Built in the 1790s, Northleach's prison was the first detention centre to segregate dangerous criminals from petty offenders.

Northleach provided the setting for the BBC production of JK Rowling's novel *The Casual Vacancy*, with the charming Market Place being transformed into the pretty fictional town of Pagford.

Carefully read through the passage on the previous page and circle the correct answers below.

1 Where is Bath situated in relation to the Cotswolds?

A. Bath is to the north-east of the Cotswolds.

B. Bath is to the south-west of the Cotswolds.

C. Bath is to the north-west of the Cotswolds.

D. Bath is to the south-east of the Cotswolds.

2 Which national newspaper has named one of the Cotswold's towns as one of the best places in the country to live?

A. *The Daily Express*

B. *The Mail on Sunday*

C. *The Independent*

D. *The Sunday Times*

3 Which location in the Cotswolds attracts the most visitors?

A. Bourton-on-the-Water

B. Burford

C. Northleach

D. Nailsworth

4 Why do you think that Nailsworth attracts so many lovers of good cuisine?

A. Because there is a glut of cheap cafes in the town

B. Because the town boasts numerous award-winning restaurants

C. Because there is ample free car parking available

D. Because there are three popular museums in Nailsworth

/4

5 What was different about the prison in Northleach?

A. It was the first prison where each prisoner had his or her own cell.

B. It was the first female-only detention centre.

C. It was the first 'open' prison, where inmates could go home in the evenings.

D. It pioneered the separation of petty villains from more dangerous prisoners.

---

6 Near which Cotswold town is there said to be a house that is haunted?

A. Burford

B. Nailsworth

C. Northleach

D. Bourton-on-the-Water

---

7 Which river runs through Bourton-on-the-Water?

A. The River Thames

B. The River Bourton

C. The River Windrush

D. The River Dart

---

8 How many years did it take Forest Green Rovers to finally win promotion to the English Football League?

A. 128 years

B. 98 years

C. 108 years

D. 118 years

/4

9 Which of the following statements is true?

Option 1   Cotswold stone is still in demand for repairs and new building projects.

Option 2   Burford celebrates Levellers' Day every year in May.

Option 3   Northleach's Market Place is said to be haunted by ghosts of ex-prisoners.

Option 4   Burford has its own town crier.

A. Options 2 and 3

B. Options 3 and 4

C. Options 1 and 2

D. Options 1, 2 and 4

---

10 Which of the following statements is not true?

Option 1   Oxford is situated to the west of Burford.

Option 2   The Queen has had her own bespoke perfume made in Northleach.

Option 3   Many of Nailsworth's former mills have been redeveloped into homes.

Option 4   Some of the leaders of the Levellers were shot.

A. Options 1 and 2

B. Options 2 and 3

C. Option 2 only

D. Options 1 and 4

---

11 Which Cotswold town also has the accolade of being the country's smallest town?

A. Bourton-on-the-Water

B. Nailsworth

C. Northleach

D. Burford

/3

12 What is the name of the country's oldest chemist's shop?

A. Reavley's

B. Cheveley's

C. Chesterton's

D. Cromwell's

---

13 How often does the farmers' market take place in Nailsworth?

A. Only on bank holidays

B. Every fortnight

C. Once a week, on a Friday

D. About every four weeks

---

14 Whereabouts in London will you find St Martin's Theatre?

A. In the East End

B. In the West End

C. In St John's Wood

D. In London next to The Shard

---

15 Which type of material is Cotswold stone?

A. Slate

B. Limestone

C. Sandstone

D. Granite

/4

Comprehension 4

Gibraltar

Gibraltar is located at the southern tip of Spain, at the point where the Atlantic Ocean meets the Mediterranean Sea. Its shoreline measures a mere 12 kilometres in total and there are two distinct sides to territory: the east side where Sandy Bay and Catalan Bay are located, and the west side, which is where the vast majority of the permanent population resides.

5   Gibraltar's location and Mediterranean climate has led to it becoming home to a wide variety of flora and fauna. Rare and exotic species of whales, fish and turtles inhabit the waters that surround the peninsula. Gibraltar is renowned for its ever-abundant population of wild but friendly dolphins, with more transient dolphins visiting the bay and Straits of Gibraltar for food, shelter and to breed in their thousands. The playful cetaceans can be found in various haunts around the coast, where they feed on sardines, herring
10 and squid and have been known to dive to a depth of about 280 metres.

Designing a fully functioning airport into an area of land that measures just 2.3 square miles was never going to be an easy mission, but Gibraltarians solved the issue with a novel answer. The airport which serves this tiny British overseas territory has made full use of the minimal space and lack of flat land available by building its only runway through the heart of the peninsula's busiest road. Consequently,
15 several times a day, any cars travelling along Winston Churchill Avenue must stop to allow planes to take off and land. Gibraltar's airport is also one of the world's scariest for air passengers, as its location leaves it exposed to high winds, making winter landings particularly bumpy.

The Gibraltar Barbary monkeys are undoubtedly the most popular visitor attraction in Gibraltar. These curious primates often will travel in troops into the town centre where tourists are amazed to witness
20 them climbing up on to people's shoulders. Legend has it that if the monkeys ever leave Gibraltar, the territory will cease to be in the hands of the British.

The 400-metre-tall limestone rock known as the Rock of Gibraltar always leaves a very powerful first impression on visitors to the peninsula. Whether approaching by land, sea or air, the lofty Rock looms pronounced and isolated as it towers over the region. The Rock is honeycombed on the inside with a
25 32-mile-long network of once-secret tunnels. In 1940, Britain was at war with Germany and Italy and the future looked bleak for Gibraltar as the enemy armies began to surround it. British Prime Minister Winston Churchill and his military leaders believed that an attack on Gibraltar was imminent and decided that the best solution was to evacuate all women and children and to create an impenetrable fortress within the Rock, capable of housing many thousands of men and soldiers with sufficient
30 provisions to withstand a prolonged siege.

St Michael's Cave has interested visitors to Gibraltar ever since Roman times. Legend has it that the cave was bottomless, resulting in the belief that Gibraltar was linked to the north of Africa by a secret subterranean passage over 24.5km in length. During World War II, a makeshift emergency hospital was built in the cave, but ultimately it wasn't necessary to be utilised as such. Later that same year,
35 while excavators were blasting an alternative entrance to the cave, a small lake was discovered in a lower chamber and christened Lower St Michael's Cave.

Carefully read through the passage on the previous page and circle the correct answers below.

1 Where do most of the inhabitants of Gibraltar live?

A. East Gibraltar

B. Sandy Bay

C. West Gibraltar

D. Catalan Bay

___

2 To which country does Gibraltar belong?

A. None, it's is an independent country.

B. Spain

C. Britain

D. Italy

___

3 What is a group of monkeys known as?

A. A primate

B. A herd

C. A flock

D. A troop

___

4 What species of mammal is the dolphin?

A. Crustacean

B. Cetacean

C. Marsupial

D. Primate

/4

5   Which thoroughfare has the heaviest traffic in Gibraltar?

A. Eastern Avenue

B. Southern Avenue

C. North-South Street

D. Winston Churchill Avenue

---

6   What do Gibraltarians believe may happen if the monkeys ever abandon Gibraltar?

A. Gibraltar will no longer be British.

B. The Spanish will invade the Gibraltar.

C. They will be beset with bad luck for ten years.

D. The tourism industry in Gibraltar will collapse.

---

7   What is hidden inside the Rock of Gibraltar?

A. A secret hospital used during World War I

B. Caves containing weapons left over from World War II

C. Lookout points to monitor possible invasions from Italy

D. A myriad of secret passageways

---

8   When can landing at Gibraltar airport be particularly uncomfortable?

A. March to May

B. June to August

C. September to November

D. December to February

/4

9 Which of the following statements is not true?

Option 1   The dolphin population in Gibraltar is buoyed every year by migrating dolphins.

Option 2   Gibraltar has two small airports, one on the east side of the territory, the other on the west side of the territory.

Option 3   The monkeys are mostly friendly and relate very well to humans.

Option 4   Winston Churchill was a prominent world leader in 1940.

A. Option 1 only

B. Option 2 only

C. Options 2 and 3

D. Options 1 and 4

---

10 Which of the following statements is not true?

Option 1   Gibraltar's shoreline is less than ten kilometres long.

Option 2   The Gibraltar dolphins feed on squid and other fish.

Option 3   Dolphins have been known to dive down more than 250 metres.

Option 4   St Michael's Cave was used as an emergency hospital during World War II.

A. Option 1 only

B. Options 1 and 2

C. Options 1 and 4

D. Options 3 and 4

---

11 What attracts most visitors in Gibraltar?

A. The wild and playful dolphins

B. The inquisitive monkeys

C. The spectacular Rock of Gibraltar

D. The wide variety of birds

/3

12 To which group of mammals do the Gibraltar monkeys belong?

A. Amphibians

B. Marsupials

C. Primates

D. Cetaceans

---

13 What happened to the Gibraltarian women and children during World War II?

A. The children were evacuated and the women worked in the hospital.

B. They were transported to other countries for their own safety.

C. They moved into the newly built fortress in the Rock.

D. They stayed in their homes to support the men in the war effort.

---

14 When was Lower St Michael's Cave discovered?

A. When workers were using excavator to create another route into St Michael's Cave.

B. A team of archaeologists discovered it while digging for clues to establish the age of St Michael's Cave.

C. When it was bombed during World War II.

D. When its use was changed to an emergency hospital.

---

15 In folklore, how was Gibraltar once joined to Africa?

A. By an underwater road

B. By a secret underwater bridge

C. By a coral reef

D. By a secret underground tunnel

/4

The Museum of Liverpool

The Liverpool Echo

The new Museum of Liverpool finally opened its doors for the first time this morning. Schoolboy Finn Liang wielded a giant pair of scissors and snipped a huge scarlet ribbon to formally open the futuristic building to members of the public. The man behind the ambitious five-year project, Philip Bond, said "This exciting new museum is all about Liverpool; we need to remind the world about our great city's historical importance and its massive contribution to popular culture and sport."

Conservative estimates expect that the new Mann Island landmark will attract up to 800,000 visitors annually.

Many of the first visitors through the doors were anxious to explore the most impressive galleries – The People's Republic and The Wonder Place – which are situated at the top of the elliptical stairs on the second floor.

However, today's well-attended celebrations were somewhat marred by a large, vociferous group of protestors. The demonstrators are angered by the new museum's suggested admission charges.

Mr Bond, who has put up £20m of his personal fortune to help fund the £72m project, proposes that the new museum should charge adults £15 each for admission but that children should be able to gain entrance for free.

Objectors welcome free admission for children but argue that if parents are charged high prices, this will inevitably deter family visits, especially from the poor and those families who perhaps do not prize cultural education so highly.

Their contention is that parents have an important role to play in further broadening their children's horizons through museum visits, in addition to other kinds of imaginative and intellectual pursuits. Museums have the potential to inspire learning in the young and can lead to an increased sense of wonder and a desire to learn and explore further.

James O'Dowd, spokesman for the demonstrators, said "It's just not fair; museums should be free to all."

Museums Should Charge for Admission

If museums are funded entirely by the state, the huge pressure on government budgets to meet the demands of hospitals, schools and police will result in underfunding and poorer museums. It is the excellence of the exhibits as opposed to the cost of visiting attractions that ultimately lures visitors to this country.

Tourists pay no income tax in this country and would be gaining a free, enriching experience at the expense of taxpayers. If free museum entry were to be considered a cultural right, shouldn't the government provide free theatre tickets as well?

Mr Bill Jones, via email

Museums Should Be Free for All to Use

Museums should be completely funded by the government and be free for all visitors as they have a very valuable role to play in preserving and imparting a nation's rich history and heritage to future generations. Free access will encourage more people to visit museums and discover more about their country. Exhibits on display in our museums reveal our artistic, political, social and scientific heritage. It should be a right for all to have free access to such resources as part of a proactive citizenship.

Revenue from tourism is hugely important to our economy and many visitors will be deterred from visiting our country if they think it will be very expensive to visit its great museums and national galleries. Tourists obviously contribute hugely to government revenues through the indirect taxes they pay and the thousands of extra jobs that they generate.

Mr James O'Dowd, via email

Carefully read through the passage on the previous page and circle the correct answers below.

1 How long did the new museum take to construct, from planning to completion?

A. Ten years

B. Seven years

C. Just one year

D. Five years

---

2 Which one of the following statements is not true?

A. Philip Bond has personally contributed more than a quarter of the entire construction costs of the project.

B. Exhibits in The Wonder Place gallery can be viewed on the museum's ground floor.

C. Mr O'Dowd thinks that everyone should be able to access the nation's heritage for free.

D. Mr Jones believes that if the government were to fund every museum, health, education and crime-fighting would take priority, resulting in museums being greatly deprived financially.

---

3 Where in the city is the new Museum of Liverpool located?

A. Mann Island

B. Adjacent to the iconic Liver Building

C. On a 20-acre site near to the redeveloped docks

D. Between the historic town hall and the famous Cavern Club

---

4 If the new Museum of Liverpool were to press ahead with its plans to charge admission fees, how much would it cost for four adults and three children to visit?

A. £45

B. £48

C. £60

D. £75

/4

5 Which of the following words or phrases best describes the design of the new museum?

A. Functional

B. Georgian

C. Classical

D. Ahead of its time

---

6 Who does Mr O'Dowd think should subsidise the country's museums?

A. Tourists

B. The banks

C. The state

D. Schools and colleges

---

7 'However, today's well-attended celebrations were somewhat marred...'

What does the word 'marred' mean in this context?

A. Disturbed

B. Confused

C. Enlivened

D. Spoiled

---

8 What does Mr Jones consider to be the principal reason that visitors are drawn to museums?

A. The fact that there is ample, free car parking at most museums

B. The high quality of the items on display

C. The fact that children are generally admitted for free

D. The fact that there are affordable hotels and restaurants near most museums

/4

9 According to the newspaper article, how might a visit to a museum inspire a young person?

Option 1   It can help to develop a sense of curiosity in a child's mind.

Option 2   Children are able to buy exciting games in the museum shop.

Option 3   It can broaden a child's horizons.

Option 4   It can motivate a child to want to learn more about the world.

A. Option 1 only

B. Option 2 only

C. Options 1, 3 and 4

D. Options 2 and 4

---

10 Which of the following statements is not true?

Option 1   Mr Bond's chief concern is that he feels tourists should be encouraged to visit our museums as they help to boost the economy.

Option 2   The city calculates that in excess of three-quarters of a million visitors will be drawn annually to the new Museum of Liverpool.

Option 3   Tourists are subject to paying income tax when they visit Britain.

Option 4   Mr Jones argues that if museums are to be free of charge, then maybe other forms of leisure should be free too.

A. Option 2 only

B. Options 1, 2 and 4

C. Option 3 only

D. Options 2 and 4

---

11 Which colour ribbon was cut to mark the opening of the new Museum of Liverpool?

A. Bright red

B. Deep blue

C. Bright yellow

D. Verdant green

/3

12 Which word best describes the mood of the demonstrators at the opening ceremony?

A. Chaotic

B. Irate

C. Unruly

D. Purposeful

---

13 'Their contention is that parents have an important role to play...'

What does the word 'contention' mean in this context?

A. Opinion

B. Discussion

C. Idea

D. Argument

---

14 What shape is the staircase leading up to The People's Republic gallery?

A. It is circular.

B. The staircase is straight.

C. It is oval shaped.

D. It is 'S' shaped.

---

15 Which one of the following statements is not true?

A. Liverpool is a large town in the north of England.

B. The final decision on whether to charge for admission has not yet been made.

C. The new museum was declared open by a school pupil.

D. Objectors argue that admission charges will discriminate against poorer families.

/4

Comprehension 6

The Great Plague and the Village of Eyam

When Charles II acceded to the throne, London was a filthy, overcrowded city. Rats thrived in the squalid, grimy conditions and diseases tended to spread very rapidly. In the blazing summer of 1665, just four years after Charles was crowned, the capital was ravaged by a deadly disease known as the bubonic plague. Black rats carried the germs in fleas on their fur and then transmitted the disease to humans when they bit them.

5 Within days of being bitten, black blotches and huge, painful lumps would appear on the victims' bodies. Sometimes their fingers, toes and even their noses turned black and fell off. They would then writhe in agony for days before succumbing to the notoriously fatal disease. A large red cross would then be painted on the doors of the dead to warn others to stay away. Night watchmen locked and kept guard over infected houses and many citizens simply starved to death as they were forbidden to leave their homes to find food.

10 Those who were able to – including the monarch, doctors, lawyers and rich merchants – fled the city to the safety of the countryside. In the capital, many charlatans established themselves as 'doctors' and gullible Londoners paid exorbitant prices for plague 'cures'. Plague water was the most popular-selling 'cure', and powdered unicorn horn and frogs' legs were also widely available. People were confidently advised that placing the tail feathers of a live chicken on the victim's skin would successfully draw out the poison,

15 resulting in a full recovery. Other procedures were also carried out in an effort to keep the plague at bay; when money was exchanged in shops, it was immersed in a quantity of malt vinegar in an effort to sterilise the coins. At markets, meat was not handed over by hand but was attached to a hook in order to avoid contact between the market traders and their customers.

This was the worst outbreak of the plague in England since the Black Death of 1348. London lost roughly
20 15% of its population. While 68,596 deaths were recorded in the city, the true number was probably well in excess of 100,000.

Although the Great Plague was responsible for unprecedented numbers of fatalities in the capital, the Derbyshire mining village of Eyam also suffered. In late August 1665, the village tailor, George Vicars, ordered a length of cloth to be sent up from London for him to make into clothes to sell in his shop. When
25 the parcel duly arrived, Vicars was frustrated to note that it was damp, so he hung it out to dry in front of the fire. Unbeknown to him, when the cloth had dried out, thousands of plague infested fleas were released into the air. Just seven days later, Vicars became the first to succumb to the Black Death in the village.

The plague quickly took a hold and began to spread swiftly through the village. The local priest, William Mompesson, decided to hold a special emergency church service where the main topic of discussion and
30 prayer was the outbreak of the plague. During the service, Mompesson asked the villagers of Eyam to agree to remain within the confines of their village to try to minimise the spread of the plague across the county. The priest was stunned to receive no opposition to his plea and the people of Eyam valiantly agreed to stay put. The gallant villagers set an astonishing example of sacrifice by sealing off their village from the surrounding areas. The generous Earl of Devonshire, who lived nearby at Chatsworth House, freely donated
35 food and medical supplies. The brave villagers paid a high price for their courage: out of a total of some 350 inhabitants, 259 died.

Nowadays, Eyam has become a magnet for tourists, due to the village's infamous association with the Great Plague of London.

Carefully read through the passage on the previous page and circle the correct answers below.

1 Prior to the Great Plague, when did England suffer a catastrophic epidemic of the plague?

A. The 13th century

B. The 15th century

C. The 14th century

D. In Victorian times

---

2 In which year was Charles II crowned?

A. 1665

B. 1661

C. 1659

D. 1662

---

3 In London, which product was the best-selling 'cure' for the plague?

A. Plague water

B. Powdered unicorn horn

C. Frogs' legs

D. Chicken feathers

---

4 Which of the following statements is not true?

A. It is likely the total number of fatalities in London was grossly under-reported.

B. Plague victims sometimes lost their blackened fingers and toes.

C. Coins were purified in vinegar during the plague.

D. Captain Devonshire lived at Chatsworth House.

/4

5 Which of the following statements is not true?

A. A cross would be painted on the door of a house where a death from plague had occurred in the capital.

B. Plague 'cures' were available free of charge to all Londoners.

C. Meat traders took care not to handle their produce during the plague.

D. More than a tenth of the population of London lost their lives in the Great Plague.

---

6 'They would then writhe in agony for days before succumbing to the notoriously fatal disease.'

What does the word 'writhe' mean in this context?

A. Scream

B. Squirm

C. Lie

D. Suffer

---

7 What was striking about the weather in the capital during the summer of 1665?

A. There was much more rainfall than was typical.

B. It was unusually chilly.

C. It was swelteringly hot.

D. Snow fell for the first time in over 20 years.

---

8 Which of the following statements is true?

A. The gallant villagers of Eyam lost slightly less than half of their population to the plague.

B. George Vicars had to put his bale of cloth outside on the washing line to dry.

C. Free food supplies were regularly donated by Chatsworth House.

D. William Mompesson decided to hold his weekly church services at a nearby village for the duration of the plague.

/4

9 Which of the following words would best describe the city of London in the 1660s?

Option 1   Densely populated

Option 2   Quaint

Option 3   Dirty

Option 4   Serene

A. Options 1 and 3

B. Options 2 and 3

C. Options 1, 2 and 3

D. Options 1 and 4

---

10 Which groups of people were able to flee the capital as the Great Plague began to take hold?

Option 1   The sovereign

Option 2   The majority of the medical profession

Option 3   Lawyers

Option 4   Wealthy traders

A. Option 2 only

B. Options 1, 2, 3 and 4

C. Options 2 and 4

D. Options 1, 2 and 4

---

11 By what other name was the plague known?

A. The Black Death

B. The Grim Death

C. The Black Epidemic

D. The Red Disease

/3

12 In which county is the village of Eyam?

A. Devon

B. Yorkshire

C. Derbyshire

D. Lincolnshire

---

13 What is the major industry of Eyam nowadays?

A. Lead mining

B. Farming

C. Quarrying

D. Tourism

---

14 What was the occupation of the first victim of the plague in the village of Eyam?

A. Miner

B. Tailor

C. Carpenter

D. Farmer

---

15 What colour were the rodents that carried the fleas which caused the plague to spread?

A. Grey

B. Brown

C. White

D. Black

/4

Comprehension 7

The Isles of Scilly

The Isles of Scilly lie 28 miles south-west of Land's End – the southern tip of the UK – and are mostly owned and leased back to the Scillonians by the Duchy of Cornwall. Their history has been one of people living off the land and sea, but the main industry is now tourism. The climate is mild all year round; frost and snowfall are rare and the islands are a haven for discovering exotic flora and fauna. The Scilly Isles are

5 warmed by the Gulf Stream in the summer months, but in winter their exposure to the fierce Atlantic winds mean the islands can be lashed by spectacular gales. Historically, there have been more shipwrecks in the seas surrounding the Isles of Scilly than anywhere else in the world. Temperatures on the Scilly Isles are slightly cooler than on the mainland and the hottest summer temperature ever recorded was 27.8°C on the islands' only runway at St Mary's in July 1987.

10 Rowing is a highly competitive sport on Scilly, carrying on the traditions of the past when pilots in small rowing boats, called gigs, would guide large vessels through the highly dangerous waters between the islands. Nowadays, there is pilot gig racing every week during the summer and the famous annual World Pilot Gig Championships helps to boost revenue for the Isles of Scilly as competitors from all over the globe descend upon the islands. The Isles of Scilly also boast the smallest football league in the world. The league consists of

15 two clubs that share the same ground, Garrison Field. The Garrison Gunners and Woolpack Wanderers play each other a total of 17 times each season and compete for two cups in addition to the league title.

St Mary's is Scilly's largest and most populous island and the only island to have any public highways. Its central hub is Hugh Town with its cluster of shops, banks, churches, a post office, cafes, galleries, pubs and restaurants, as well as a museum. It has three beaches in very close proximity: Porthcressa, which is popular

20 with beachcombers; Town Beach, a perfect spot from which to watch the *Scillonian III* dock daily on the Quay; and Porthmellon, which also hosts the Sailing Centre. Old Town is the other major settlement on St Mary's, with its own beautiful beach, Pelistry Bay, and its picturesque church and churchyard where Harold Wilson is buried.

Tresco is the second largest of the islands and is the only one of the Scillies to be privately owned. There are

25 dramatic rocky outcrops, Bronze Age burial sites, castle ruins, secluded sandy beaches and the world-famous Tresco Abbey Garden, which was established in the 1830s by Augustus Smith. This horticultural paradise hosts a spectacular collection of more than 20,000 exotic plants from all corners of the world, many of which cannot be grown anywhere else in Britain.

Bryher is the smallest of the Scilly Isles. The aptly named 'Hell Bay' on the west coast – so called after the

30 dramatic number of shipwrecks and deaths that have taken place there in the past – has now given its name to arguably the most luxurious hotel on the Isles of Scilly.

St Martin's boasts an award-winning beach, from where colonies of seals can easily be spotted near the shore. The clarity of the waters makes snorkelling and diving with seals popular with locals and visitors alike. It is the first island you spot as you cross from the mainland and the third largest of the Scilly Isles. The hundred or so

35 inhabitants are industrious people – there's a flower farm and a thriving vineyard.

On the most south-westerly edge of the Isles of Scilly, St Agnes is totally unspoilt and peaceful; it is the least developed and populous of the five inhabited islands and has no hotel or other places to stay. A huge lighthouse stands at the island's highest point.

Carefully read through the passage on the previous page and circle the correct answers below.

1 What were the main industries on the Isles of Scilly before tourism became the major source of income?

A. Farming and fishing

B. Wine making and timber production

C. Coal and tin mining

D. Coffee and tea production

2 Which powerful current in the Atlantic Ocean is responsible for the mild climate on the Isles of Scilly?

A. The Roaring Forties

B. The Jet Stream

C. The Gulf Stream

D. The North Atlantic Drift

3 What is the name of the passenger ferry that makes daily trips to the Isles of Scilly?

A. *Scilly* III

B. *Scillonian* III

C. *St Mary* III

D. *Scillas* III

4 How many beaches are there in total on St Mary's?

A. Five

B. Three

C. Four

D. Eight

/4

5 Which island has the smallest number of inhabitants?

A. St Martin's

B. Bryher

C. St Agnes

D. Tresco

---

6 Where is former Prime Minister Wilson laid to rest?

A. In Hell Bay on the island of Bryher

B. In a churchyard in Old Town, St Mary's

C. Next to the nature reserve on St Mary's

D. In the grounds of the botanical gardens on Tresco

---

7 Why do you think that the waters of St Martin's would be the best place to enjoy snorkelling with seals?

A. The temperature is slightly warmer.

B. There are a much greater number of seals in the area.

C. The clarity of the water would make for a better view underwater.

D. The seals in the waters of St Martin's are much more tame and friendly.

---

8 What is a popular activity at Porthcressa beach on the island of St Mary's?

A. It is a perfect spot to watch the boats coming and going.

B. It is popular with people searching for artefacts washed ashore.

C. People love to dine in the many seafood restaurants.

D. People like to look for rare birds, especially puffins.

/4

9   Which of the following statements is true?

Option 1   The Isles of Scilly football teams compete in two cups and a league each season.

Option 2   The gardens on Tresco were founded in the 19th century.

Option 3   Tresco is the third largest of the Scilly Isles.

Option 4   St Martin's has won a prestigious award for its stunning beach.

A. Option 1 only

B. Options 1 and 2

C. Options 2 and 4

D. Options 1, 2 and 4

---

10   Which of the following statements is not true?

Option 1   St Agnes is the most north-westerly of all the Isles of Scilly.

Option 2   Grapes are grown on the island of St Martin's.

Option 3   It seldom snows on the Isles of Scilly.

Option 4   The Isles of Scilly lie fewer than 20 miles from Land's End.

A. Option 2 only

B. Option 3 only

C. Options 2 and 4

D. Options 1 and 4

---

11   Who owns the vast majority of the Isles of Scilly?

A. The British government

B. Augustus Smith

C. The Duchy of Cornwall

D. The county of Cornwall

/3

12 What might your accommodation be if you were to stay overnight on St Agnes?

A. Possibly a tent

B. Probably a five-star boutique hotel

C. Maybe an inexpensive hostel

D. Perhaps a quaint traditional guest house

---

13 At which football ground do the Garrison Gunners team play their away games?

A. Garrison Field

B. Hunter Hill

C. Woolpack Ground

D. Hugh Town Lane

---

14 Where is the most opulent holiday accommodation on the Isles of Scilly?

A. The Flying Boat Cottage on St Agnes

B. The New Inn at the docks on St Mary's

C. St Martin's campsite

D. The Hell Bay Hotel on the island of Bryher

---

15 Where do the contestants for the World Pilot Gig Championships hail from?

A. The mainland

B. France and Spain

C. Scandinavia

D. All over the world

/4

Comprehension 8

Queen Mary 2 Cruise

The sheer scale and elegance of Cunard's *Queen Mary 2* make it the most famous ocean liner in the world. The ship boasts 15 restaurants, five swimming pools, a full-sized theatre, a casino, a spa, a 3D cinema and the largest dance floor at sea. Like her sister ships, *Queen Victoria* and *Queen Elizabeth*, the liner has a traditional promenade deck which circumnavigates the ship.

5   The *Queen Mary 2* will depart from her home port of Southampton on New Year's Day to begin a luxury round-the-world epic voyage. Leaving the UK's January chill in her wake, the ship will first set sail for Madeira, which is renowned for its warm-all-year-round climate. The tiny island in the Atlantic Ocean is famous for its cake, lace and wicker goods. After an overnight stay, the ship will then sail around 500km south and will call briefly at the island of Tenerife, which is home to Mount Teide, Spain's highest mountain.

10 The next port of call will be Cape Town in South Africa, where passengers can take in stunning views of the iconic Table Mountain. There will be an opportunity to take part in a safari during our four-night stay. Cricket fans may also want to visit St George's Park, the sixth-oldest cricket venue in the world.

Forging on over the Indian Ocean, the ship will pass by the French-owned island of Réunion, home to an interesting vanilla plantation and one of the world's most active volcanoes – Le Piton de la Fournaise. 15 Next stop will be the island of Mauritius, where the luxury liner will dock for seven idyllic days. The waters surrounding Mauritius are calm and clear, which make it an ideal location for snorkelling. The *Queen Mary 2* then spans almost 6000 kilometres of open ocean before cruising along the Margaret River on its approach to Perth in Western Australia.

The liner will spend three weeks in Australia, docking twelve times and visiting all six states. Passengers will 20 begin to appreciate the enormous scale of this vast country, and be struck by the differences between the rugged, sparsely populated west, and the busy cities such as Sydney in the east. Prior to leaving the Antipodes, the *Queen Mary 2* will visit the island of Tasmania, once home to the notorious Port Arthur penal colony.

The ship will then head north to Asia, docking firstly in the former British colony of Hong Kong, where the bustle of the Temple Street Night Market is always chaotic; technology stalls ply for trade alongside street 25 sellers offering more traditional items like jade carvings and antiques. Every night, the world's largest light and sound show, 'Symphony of Lights', creates a spectacle of music and illuminations that involve some 40 buildings around the famous harbour.

The next port of call for the *Queen Mary 2* will be Dubai in the United Arab Emirates. It is difficult to imagine that, as recently as half a century ago, this superlative city was a humble village with a main industry 30 of pearl fishing. Over recent years, extraordinary projects have come to define Dubai: enormous man-made islands in the shape of palm trees; the iconic seven-star Burj Al Arab hotel; and the Burj Khalifa, the world's tallest building, which stands over half a mile high.

After the *Queen Mary 2* has cruised through the Suez Canal into the Mediterranean, she will dock briefly in Naples, where ancient Pompeii's final moments are forever preserved in the ash that covered the city from 35 the erupting Vesuvius in the year AD79. Passengers may choose to hop across to the isle of Capri, the one-time playground of wealthy Romans, or opt to soak in the beauty of Sorrento and the Amalfi Coast. The majestic ship's final port of call will be Lisbon, Portugal's capital, with an intense North-African heritage and a rich history of daring exploration. It is certain to be an emotional finale to the *Queen Mary 2*'s world adventure.

Carefully read through the passage on the previous page and circle the correct answers below.

1 How many sister ships does the *Queen Mary 2* have?

A. None

B. Two

C. One

D. Three

2 In which season will the world cruise commence?

A. Spring

B. Summer

C. Autumn

D. Winter

3 In which ocean is the island of Madeira?

A. The Atlantic Ocean

B. The Pacific Ocean

C. The Indian Ocean

D. The Southern Ocean

4 On which island is Spain's tallest peak?

A. Madeira

B. Cape Verde

C. Tenerife

D. Mauritius

/4

5 On which island did affluent Italians once prefer to congregate?

A. Corsica

B. Capri

C. Sicily

D. Malta

---

6 How many places are there to have a meal or a drink on board the ship?

A. 10

B. 15

C. 12

D. 20

---

7 From which material are the carvings at the Temple Street Night Market made?

A. Wood

B. Onyx

C. Marble

D. Jade

---

8 Where will the *Queen Mary 2* next dock after leaving Cape Town?

A. The island of Réunion

B. The island of Mauritius

C. Le Piton de la Fournaise

D. Port Elizabeth

/4

9   Which of the following statements is true?

Option 1   Madeira cake is famous throughout the world.

Option 2   Australia is often referred to as being in the 'antipodes'.

Option 3   Madeira is approximately 500km north of Tenerife.

Option 4   St George's Park is the oldest cricket ground in the world.

A. Option 1 only

B. Options 2 and 3

C. Options 1, 2 and 3

D. Options 1 and 3

---

10   Which of the following statements is true?

Option 1   There was once an infamous penal colony on the island of Tasmania.

Option 2   The waters surrounding the island of Mauritius are noted for their clarity.

Option 3   There are 12 states in Australia.

Option 4   There is a vast coffee plantation on the island of Réunion.

A. Options 1 and 2

B. Option 2 only

C. Options 1 and 3

D. Options 1, 2 and 4

/2

Comprehension 9

Autonomous Cars

By the year 2030 you may well be making car journeys in vehicles that are capable of moving, steering, navigating and parking without any human input at all. These autonomous cars will be fitted with sophisticated radar equipment, capable of reading road signs and automatically sense all obstacles in their path.

The most significant benefit of this technology is the expected reduction in road traffic accidents. Extensive
5   research has shown that driver error is responsible for 93% of incidents on the nation's roads. When cars are able to drive themselves, the roads would become much safer. There would be no more drink-driving, no phone calls or texting while at the wheel and careless or incompetent driving would cease to exist. Fewer accidents on the roads would mean that there would be major improvements to traffic flow and most journeys would take less time.

10   Another huge benefit autonomous cars will offer is full mobility to people who currently cannot drive and have limited or no access to public transport. These people would be able to pursue activities outside the home or visit restaurants and shops more often, thereby providing a boost to the economy. The freight industry would be transformed and become much more efficient if lorries could operate for almost 24 hours per day; lorry drivers currently may only drive for six hours before they are required by law to take a break.

15   Some experts have predicted that the introduction of driverless cars may see a drastic reduction in domestic flights. Currently, if you wish to fly from London to Edinburgh the actual flight takes only one hour, but with the time taken to drive to the airport, in addition to the time spent parking your car, plus the time taken to check in for your flight, the actual journey time is a lot longer. Autonomous vehicles will enable travellers to leave home in the evening at 11pm and arrive safely the next morning at 7am after a refreshing night's sleep in
20   the car.

The computer systems installed in autonomous cars will be required to be 100% reliable and accurate. Should the software crash or be hacked, the vehicle may begin moving at an incorrect speed or in the wrong direction. Another potential complication involves the environment in which the driverless car is travelling. Roads vary wildly; a newly built dual carriageway with clearly defined white lines and road signs will result in ideal
25   conditions for autonomous cars, but over time, the white lines will wear away and roadworks will affect the surface of the roads. Narrow country lanes could present yet another challenge for autonomous cars. There are rarely any white lines defining the edges of these rural roads, making it extremely difficult for the vehicle to be able to 'see' where the tarmac ends and the grass begins. All of the country's roads are subject to speed restrictions, which raises the question of an autonomous vehicle's handling of road conditions. It is not yet
30   known if a driverless car would be constantly trying to attain the maximum speed limit on each journey, irrespective of road conditions. All of these scenarios will need to be thoroughly trialled before full autonomy can be expected to work as effectively as a driver at the wheel.

Government officials, transport authorities and engineers have decided that there will be five steps in the road to full autonomy. Stage two is complete, where some of the driver's tasks are automated and assisted – like
35   navigation and parking. The technology is currently at stage three, where cars are permitted to take control on certain roads, such as motorways, but with the driver ready to retake control. Stage five will be reached when cars are wholly autonomous and drivers are no longer necessary. The most complicated part of this journey will be the period when there are both cars driven by humans and driverless vehicles on the roads. Eventually, humans driving themselves will become an expensive luxury as insurance premiums will be significantly lower
40   for autonomous cars.

Carefully read through the passage on the previous page and circle the correct answers below.

1 What is the most compelling reason for having fully autonomous vehicles on the roads?

A. The number of accidents would be dramatically reduced.

B. The cost of a new car would be likely to be much cheaper.

C. There would be fewer vehicles on the roads.

D. There would be fewer cyclists on the roads.

2 What percentage of road traffic accidents are deemed to be the result of driver error?

A. About half of all accidents

B. Just a quarter

C. More than 90%

D. All of them

3 What will probably be the most significant shortcoming with an autonomous vehicle?

A. The reliability of its computer system and software

B. Its braking system

C. Its height from the road

D. Autonomous vehicles are likely to use much more fuel.

4 What would the introduction of fully autonomous cars eliminate?

A. Careless driving

B. Generally poor driving

C. The use of mobile phones while driving

D. All of the above

/4

5 'All of these scenarios will need to be thoroughly trialled before full autonomy can be expected to work as effectively as a driver at the wheel.'

What does the word 'scenarios' mean in this context?

A. Stages

B. Problems

C. Designs

D. Possible situations

---

6 How many steps are there going to be in the full autonomy process?

A. Two

B. Five

C. Four

D. Three

---

7 What is anticipated will be the most challenging stage on the road to full automation?

A. The time when there will be autonomous vehicles and cars driven by humans on the road at the same time

B. When there are roadworks on the motorways

C. The times when the weather is bad

D. Night times, when it is dark

---

8 Which one of the following statements is true?

A. All roads in Britain have white lines.

B. Driving classic, non-autonomous cars will attract cheaper insurance cover.

C. Hackers could cause an autonomous vehicle to change direction.

D. It won't be possible to sleep in the back of a driverless car.

/4

9 Which of the following statements is not true?

Option 1   Autonomous cars will be able to perform every driving manoeuvre except for parking.

Option 2   The freight industry will become much more efficient.

Option 3   A domestic flight from the capital to Edinburgh takes one hour.

Option 4   There are concerns about the cars' computers being hacked.

A. Option 3 only

B. Option 1 only

C. Options 1 and 3

D. Options 2 and 4

---

10 Which of the following statements is true?

Option 1   Fully autonomous cars are expected to be widespread by 2030.

Option 2   Autonomous cars will benefit those people who can't drive and who don't have access to a bus or train service.

Option 3   There will be a huge increase in passengers taking domestic flights as people try to avoid the inevitable chaos on the roads.

Option 4   Traffic will flow much better as there will be fewer hold-ups as a result of there being fewer accidents on the roads.

A. Option 1 only

B. Options 1 and 2

C. Options 1 and 4

D. Options 1, 2 and 4

---

11 For how long are lorry drivers currently permitted to drive before they must take a break?

A. 12 hours

C. 24 hours

B. 6 hours

D. 4 hours

/3

12 What enables autonomous cars to 'see' their environment?

A. Radar

B. Cameras

C. Lasers

D. All of the above

---

13 Which will be the next phase to be implemented?

A. The second stage

B. The fifth stage

C. The third stage

D. The fourth stage

---

14 Which of the following statements is not true?

A. There needs to be absolutely no margin of error on driverless cars' computer systems.

B. Autonomous cars will spell the end of drink-driving.

C. More than a quarter of the nation's roads don't have speed limits.

D. The government have been working with transport authorities to roll out the implementation of driverless cars.

---

15 How long might a journey typically take from London to Edinburgh in a driverless car?

A. 10 hours

B. 4 hours

C. 1 hour

D. 8 hours

/4

Comprehension 10

Prometheus the Fire-Giver

In the early days of the universe, the Titans ruled the Earth. Prometheus was the wisest of the Titans. He disliked the other Titans, who were always fighting, so he joined the god Zeus to overthrow them. With Prometheus's help, Zeus defeated the Titans and sent them down into Tartarus, a fiery subterranean region of torment and misery. Then Zeus took control of the Earth above.

5 When Zeus became king of the gods, the people upon the Earth were nothing more than savages. They lived in caves, wore skins of wild animals, and ate all their food raw because they did not know how to make fire.

Prometheus loved human beings and thought that they would have more success if they were given the right skills by the right teacher. Secretly, he taught the people lessons, and soon they began to think for themselves. Zeus found out what Prometheus was doing and he commanded him to stop giving the people

10 so much help, for Zeus feared that they would become too powerful. Prometheus complied with Zeus's wishes, and for some time the people continued to live in caves, unaware of how to make clothes or build a fire.

However, Prometheus did not obey Zeus for long. He soon defied the king of the gods and continued teaching and sharing knowledge with the people. He taught them to build clay huts with straw roofs, and

15 to read, write, and count. He showed them how to plant crops for food and for medicine, and how to track time by the stars. He demonstrated using animals to pull wagons and ploughs. He explained how to build ships and how to make ships go faster. The people were thankful for each new gift, and each day they asked for still more.

Finally, in his greatest gesture of defiance, Prometheus stole some of the fire kept by the gods and, concealing

20 it in the hollow stalk of a plant, brought it down to the people. From that time on, the lives of human beings improved greatly, as they began to cook their food and make things that could be created using fire.

As another gift to mankind, to prevent people from being troubled by woes and problems, Prometheus sealed up the world's sicknesses and sorrows in a storage jar that he kept safely in his house, out of reach. It seemed as if the lives of the people would soon become as free from worry as the lives of the gods.

25 When Zeus saw what Prometheus had done, he was very angry, for he did not want human beings to take on godlike pride or power. To prevent any threat from humankind, Zeus came up with a plan. He ordered that Pandora, the first woman created on Earth, be sent to live in the house of Prometheus. Pandora was naturally curious about her new surroundings, and one of the first things she did was open the storage jar to see what was inside. No sooner had she done this than all the world's troubles, so carefully sealed up by

30 Prometheus, flew out in a rush to plague the people. And they have done so ever since.

To punish Prometheus for his disobedience, Zeus had him chained to the side of a mountain, exposed to hot sun and beating rains day after day. It was only many years later that Zeus's half-mortal son Hercules took pity on Prometheus and set him free.

Because Prometheus had done so much for humankind, and because he had suffered such hardship for those

35 deeds, the Greek people were always grateful to him. But they did not build temples to him or worship him. That honour was reserved for Zeus and the other formidable gods of Mount Olympus.

Carefully read through the passage on the previous page and circle the correct answers below.

1 Who did Prometheus disapprove of?

A. The people of the Earth

C. The people of Tartarus

B. The gods of Mount Olympus

D. The Titans

2 Why did Prometheus keep his lessons secret?

A. He knew Zeus would not approve and would try to stop him.

B. He wanted to give Zeus a good surprise.

C. He was supposed to be spending his time hunting animals.

D. He didn't want too many people to ask for lessons.

3 'With Prometheus's help, Zeus defeated the Titans and sent them into Tartarus, a fiery subterranean region of torment and misery.'

What does the word 'subterranean' mean in this context?

A. Secret

C. Illegal

B. Underground

D. Enemy

4 What made the lives of the human beings considerably better?

A. Huts

C. Fire

B. Farming

D. Sailing

5 Where did Prometheus keep the world's troubles?

A. In a clay hut

C. On a mountainside

B. In a jar

D. In a cooking pot

/5

6   Which word is used in the text for the great suffering of humankind?

     A. Woes   **C.** Savages

     B. Defiance   **D.** Torment

---

7   What did Zeus want to do?

     A. Support Prometheus's ambitions

     B. Keep the human beings free from harm

     C. Test whether Pandora was trustworthy

     D. Protect his own power

---

8   What is the author's opinion about what Pandora did?

     A. It was inexcusable.   **C.** It was understandable.

     B. It was harmless.   **D.** It was wicked.

---

9   Why didn't the Greek people dedicate any temple to Prometheus?

     A. They did not build temples to people who had been punished.

     B. They thought Prometheus should have done more to help the people.

     C. They thought a temple to Prometheus would bring suffering to them.

     D. They thought that only gods deserved temples.

---

10   Why did Hercules release Prometheus from the mountainside?

     A. He felt sorry for Prometheus.   **C.** He felt grateful to Prometheus.

     B. He wanted to defeat Prometheus.   **D.** He was Prometheus's brother.

/5

The Pied Piper of Hamelin

Hamelin is a sleepy little town, spread out along the banks of a deep, wide river. Unfortunately, Hamelin had a big problem with rats: it was completely infested with them. There was not a barn or storeroom or cupboard that hadn't been eaten in to; not a cheese that the rats hadn't gnawed hollow; not a sugary treat that they hadn't gobbled up. The noise of rats hurrying and scurrying and squeaking was so loud that no-

5   one in the town could get any rest. No matter what they tried – cats, poison, rat-catchers, traps – every day there seemed to be more rats than ever. The mayor and the town council were at their wits' end.

As they were sitting in the town hall one day, a messenger brought word that a strange man was at the town gates. This stranger was tall and thin, with keen, piercing eyes. He wore a coat with all the colours of the rainbow, and he offered to get rid of the rats. 'I'm called the Pied Piper,' he began. 'What might you be

10   willing to pay me, if I rid you of every rat in your town?'

Well, much as the town's leaders feared the rats, they feared parting with their money even more. But, in the end, they promised the Pied Piper fifty crowns – a generous sum – as long as not a single rat was left to squeak in Hamelin.

Out of the hall stepped the Piper, and as he did so he laid his pipe to his lips and played a high-pitched tune.

15   Up Silver Street and down Gold Street he went, and then to the harbour, and out of every hole the rats came tumbling. As the Piper paced along, slowly and gravely, the townsfolk flocked to see him, the rats parading behind.

At the water's edge he stepped onto a boat, and as he shoved off into deep water, piping shrilly all the while, the rats followed him, splashing, paddling and wagging their tails with delight. On and on he played, until

20   the rats sank into the river's depths where they drowned. The Piper returned to the town in his boat, not a single rat in pursuit.

But as soon as the Piper stepped ashore, the mayor began to shake his head. The town's money chest had been sadly empty of late, and where were the fifty crowns going to come from? And the Piper's job had been easily accomplished – all he had done was pipe his way through town and set off in a boat.

25   'Come, my good man,' said he, 'you see what poor folk we are. We cannot pay fifty crowns! Maybe twenty crowns? When all is said and done, it will be good pay for the trouble you've taken.'

'Fifty crowns was our agreement,' said the Piper. 'And if I were you, I'd pay it quickly.'

'What will you do if we don't pay you?' asked the mayor. 'The rats are all dead. You can't bring them back.' And he turned his back on the Piper and walked away.

30   The Piper then laid his pipe to his lips and played a tune that was joyous, full of happy laughter and merry play. And as he paced down the streets, from schoolrooms and playrooms and nurseries, every child in the town ran out with eager glee and followed the Piper. Dancing, laughing and joining hands, the bright throng moved along up Gold Street and down Silver Street, and beyond Silver Street to the cool, green forest.

35   Deeper and deeper into the green wood the stranger strode and played on his pipe, the delighted children in tow. And watch and wait as they might, the townspeople never saw the Piper or their children ever again.

Carefully read through the passage on the previous page and circle the correct answers below.

1   'The mayor and the town council were at their wits' end.'

What does the expression 'at their wits' end' mean in this sentence?

A. Unable to sleep   **C.** Close to finding a solution

B. Running out of ideas   **D.** Short of food

---

2   What were the town's leaders most afraid of?

A. Rats   **C.** Losing their children

B. Spending money   **D.** The Pied Piper

---

3   Which of the following statements is true?

A. Hamelin is next to the sea.

B. A shallow river runs a short distance away from Hamelin.

C. There is a large lake near Hamelin.

D. Hamelin has a large river running through it.

---

4   What do the street names, Silver Street and Gold Street, suggest about Hamelin?

A. The buildings are made of silver and gold.

B. Hamelin is a small humble town.

C. Hamelin has probably been a wealthy town.

D. The streets are paved with silver and gold.

---

5   Which expression shows that the children followed the Pied Piper?

A. Bright throng   **C.** In tow

B. Wove in and out   **D.** Eager glee

/5

Comprehension 12

The Lake District

The Lake District is an extremely picturesque region situated in the north-west of England. The area is famous for its fells, mountains and valleys, in addition to numerous clear, freshwater lakes. The area was designated a national park in 1951 in order to safeguard the landscape from any unwanted industrial or commercial change and development. The Lake District was made a UNESCO World Heritage site in July
5　2017, joining other iconic world attractions like the Taj Mahal in India and Sydney Opera House in Australia.

In the 1920s, the village of Mardale nestled in the picturesque valley of Haweswater in the Lake District. The villagers were soon to have their lives turned upside down when permission was granted to transform the entire valley into a vast reservoir with enough capacity to supply the needs of the whole of the city of Manchester, to the south. Work began in 1929 with 200 men working on the construction of the dam. The
10　workers lived with their families in a specially built makeshift village – called Burnbanks – for the entire duration of the six-year project. When construction was complete, Mardale's hundred or so residents gathered in the village church for a final, poignant service on 18 August 1935. The Bishop of Carlisle conducted the service and more than a thousand people gathered on a nearby hillside to listen to his words via a loud speaker fastened to the church tower. After the service, graves from the churchyard were moved and buried
15　in the nearby village of Shap, to the east of Mardale. The next day, water was pumped into the newly formed reservoir and the old village was soon completely submerged.

During World War II, students from the Royal College of Art in London were evacuated to Ambleside in the Lake District and billeted in every house and barn available. Trainloads of evacuees, including curators from the Tate Gallery plus the famous works of art in their care, such as Gainsborough's 'Blue Boy', spent the entire
20　war in the Lake District.

A popular tourist destination since the end of the 18th century, the Lakeland town of Keswick became an important centre for pencil manufacture after graphite was discovered in the nearby hills just north of the town. At the start of World War II, top-secret plans were drawn up with the Cumberland Pencil Factory to create a secret map-and-compass pencil. Four tiny maps were printed on very fine paper and rolled up
25　and inserted into specially hollowed out pencil-barrel cavities. The maps detailed escape routes through Germany to the west in Belgium, and south to Switzerland. The secret map pencils were issued to all Bomber Command aircrew and also sent to prisoners of war. They became a vital cog in the wartime escape network.

Although best known for her dainty children's books with characters such as Tom Kitten,
30　Mrs Tiggy-Winkle and Jemima Puddle-Duck – which she also illustrated – Beatrix Potter became a champion of conservation in the Lake District soon after moving there from London in 1906. She bought Hill Top house and farm later that same year and started breeding sheep. She married local solicitor William Heelis, devoted herself to farming and became an expert on Herdwick sheep. As Beatrix's books became more and more successful, she bought more land and properties until ultimately she owned 14 farms and over
35　4000 acres of land. To conserve her beloved Lake District countryside, she left all her farms and land to the National Trust, with strict instructions on how she wished them to be run in the future.

There are 16 lakes in the Lake District; Windermere is probably the most famous, and at 11.2 miles it is also the longest lake in the country. England's deepest body of water is Wastwater, at an astonishing 74 metres. It is also remarkable for the fact that it contains absolutely no aquatic life whatsoever.

Carefully read through the passage on the previous page and circle the correct answers below.

1 Which one of the following statements is true?

A. Beatrix Potter moved from the Lake District back to London in 1906.

B. The dam at Haweswater took over five years to complete.

C. Each pencil given to service personnel during World War II contained two secret rolled-up maps.

D. Lake Windermere is just short of ten miles long.

2 Who was the illustrator for Beatrix Potter's children's storybooks?

A. William Heelis

B. Beatrix illustrated all her books herself.

C. Beatrix's father illustrated her books.

D. One of Beatrix's nephews

3 Why was the Lake District designated a national park?

A. To allow admission fees to be collected from the public

B. To protect the wildlife in the region

C. To protect the region from becoming spoiled by developers

D. To safeguard the area from flooding

4 'residents gathered in the village church for a final, poignant service on 18 August 1935.' What does the word 'poignant' mean in this context?

A. Sad   C. Defiant

B. Crowded   D. Spirited

5 Which word best describes the village of Burnbanks?

A. Depressing   C. Picturesque

B. Stunning   D. Temporary

/5

6 Which natural resource was mined at Keswick?

A. Coal

B. Slate

C. Graphite

D. Gold

---

7 How many residents were living in Mardale at the time of the construction of the dam?

A. Approximately two dozen

B. More than 1000

C. Around 60

D. About 100

---

8 Where was the village of Mardale in relation to Shap?

A. Mardale was to the west of Shap.

B. Mardale was to the east of Shap.

C. Mardale was to the south of Shap.

D. Mardale was to the north of Shap.

---

9 Which one of the following statements is not true?

A. The final church service at Mardale was conducted by the Bishop of Carlisle.

B. Windermere is the deepest lake in England.

C. Beatrix Potter left all her property to the National Trust.

D. Valuable paintings were 'evacuated' to the Lake District during World War II.

---

10 What is unusual about Wastwater lake?

A. It is the only lake where swimming is not permitted in the water.

B. It is unusually shallow and therefore not suitable for boats.

C. It contains incredibly high levels of salt, which makes it easy for people to float.

D. It doesn't contain any fish.

/5

My Father's War

The year is 1918, and Annie's dad is away fighting in France during World War I. When he drops out of contact, Annie and her mum travel from Australia to France to see if they can find out what has happened to him. In this extract, Annie and her friend Paul walk back into the city of Amiens on 20 April, to see whether Paul's house has survived the recent bombing. It provides a glimpse into the way that war not only kills people,
5 *but also destroys many other things.*

It was eerily quiet, with very few people in the streets, and those who were, hurried along without looking to the right or left. Army vehicles passed us, and ambulances, but otherwise there was no traffic.

Paul was hurrying now. I didn't need to look at his face to know he feared the worst.

...

When we finally reached the canal area and saw the shattered remains of what had been Little Venice, all
10 I could do was stand there and stare, aghast.

...

Paul was as shocked as I was, or more so. His face had gone grey, his eyes hard as stone, a muscle worked in his jaw, but he said nothing. Instead, he hobbled painfully forward, carefully picking his way over the sad rubble and plaster dust and blackened timbers of what had once been his home. Cat followed him, picking her way across the rubble...

15 It was a horrible mess inside. Household goods – beds, chairs, tables, clocks, dishes, vases – had been shredded and smashed by the force of the shell that had landed on the block. It must have rained too: papers, feathers from mattresses and pillows, material from curtains and other things had become soaked into a vile, pulpy, wet, stinking mass. Nothing, it seemed to me, could be saved, but Paul was grimly working his way around, as if looking for something.

...

20 I was just dusting myself down and preparing to go after him when I noticed something sticking out of the rubble at my feet, revealed by the dislodging of the bricks I had tripped on. A flash of silver.

I pulled at it and out came a photo frame, the one that used to sit on Madame Baudin's mantelpiece. The family photo of the three of them: Madame Baudin, her son, and Paul as a young child. The glass had been shattered, the silver frame scratched and battered. But the photo was still there, a little dusty but
25 otherwise unharmed.

Cat at my heels, I caught up with Paul. I didn't say anything, just handed him the photograph in its silver frame. He stopped. Looked at the photo. At me. Opened his mouth. Shut it again. I could see he was afraid that he'd start crying again if he said anything about it.

Historical Note

The city of Amiens, in the Somme Valley, was part of the Western Front during World War I. Fighting had
30 *occurred in this region throughout 1916–1917, but in 1918 the confrontation shifted. Instead of the trench warfare of 1916, battles now took place in fields, woods and ruined village streets. The final attack, which would eventually liberate the Somme, began on 8 August and was led by the great Australian general, John Monash. However, it would not be until 11 November, when the Germans finally surrendered, that this beautiful, tormented region would experience peace.*

Extract from a novel by Sophie Masson

Carefully read through the passage on the previous page and circle the correct answers below.

1 Which one of the words below from the introduction is an adjective?

A. 'friend'

B. 'happened'

C. 'destroys'

D. 'recent'

---

2 What information is not given in the text (including the introduction and historical note)?

A. Assumptions concerning the weather conditions after the bombings had taken place

B. Any details on the presence or well-being of Annie's father at the Western Front

C. The location of Annie's country of residence

D. The location of Paul's house in the city of Amiens

---

3 How did Paul react when he first saw the photograph?

A. He was delighted that it had been found.

B. He was annoyed with Annie for disturbing the room.

C. He had to fight away tears.

D. He was grateful that it was still intact.

---

4 'It was eerily quiet, with very few people…'

What does the word 'eerily' mean?

A. Strangely

B. Surprisingly

C. Really

D. Notably

---

5 Which specific items destroyed by the bomb are mentioned in the text?

A. Stools

B. Sofas

C. Timepieces

D. Bookcases

/5

6 Which one of the following statements is true?

A. Amiens is situated in the Loire Valley in France.

B. The Germans finally accepted defeat in November 1918.

C. Annie and her mother travelled to France upon receipt of a telegram from Annie's father.

D. Annie and Paul were astonished to find that the glass on the photo frame was intact.

---

7 What kinds of transport did Annie and Paul notice on the streets of Amiens?

A. Mainly buses and coaches

B. Just bicycles

C. Cars and vans

D. Just military transport and vehicles carrying the sick and injured

---

8 Of which material was the photograph frame made?

A. Silver   **C.** Gold

B. Glass   **D.** Wood

---

9 How long after Annie and Paul visited Amiens was the war finally over?

A. A little over three months   **C.** Exactly six months

B. Almost two years   **D.** Almost seven months

---

10 Which one of the following statements is true?

A. The photo that Annie found was previously on display on Madame Baudin's bookcase.

B. Paul and Annie had feline company as they surveyed the rubble.

C. Annie was overjoyed to find her father safe and well in Amiens.

D. Paul and Annie cycled through the city of Amiens to reach Paul's house.

/5

Comprehension 14

Snake

DH Lawrence wrote Snake *in about 1920 while he was living in Sicily, Italy. In it, he explores the conflicted feelings humans and wild animals often have towards each other. This is an extract from the poem.*

A snake came to my water-trough
On a hot, hot day, and I in pyjamas for the heat,
To drink there.

In the deep, strange-scented shade of the great dark carob-tree
5   I came down the steps with my pitcher
And must wait, must stand and wait, for there he was at the trough before me.

He reached down from a fissure in the earth-wall in the gloom
And trailed his yellow-brown slackness soft-bellied down, over the edge of the stone trough
And rested his throat upon the stone bottom,
10   And where the water had dripped from the tap, in a small clearness,
He sipped with his straight mouth,
Softly drank through his straight gums, into his slack long body,
Silently.

Someone was before me at my water-trough,
15   And I, like a second comer, waiting.
He lifted his head from his drinking, as cattle do,
And looked at me vaguely, as drinking cattle do,
And flickered his two-forked tongue from his lips, and mused a moment,
And stooped and drank a little more,
20   Being earth-brown, earth-golden from the burning bowels of the earth
On the day of Sicilian July, with Etna smoking.
The voice of my education said to me
He must be killed,
For in Sicily the black, black snakes are innocent, the gold are venomous.

25   And voices in me said, If you were a man
You would take a stick and break him now, and finish him off.

But must I confess how I liked him,
How glad I was he had come like a guest in quiet, to drink at my water-trough
And depart peaceful, pacified, and thankless,
30   Into the burning bowels of this earth?

Was it cowardice, that I dared not kill him?
Was it perversity, that I longed to talk to him?
Was it humility, to feel so honoured?

I felt so honoured.

D H Lawrence

Carefully read through the extract from the poem on the previous page and circle the correct answers below.

1   Which literary device is the author using in line 4 of the poem?

A. Metaphor   **C.** Allusion

B. Oxymoron   **D.** Alliteration

---

2   How does the author think that cows appear when they are drinking?

A. They look excited and refreshed.

B. They have an unclear expression on their faces.

C. They begin to look sleepy.

D. They appear to become aggressive.

---

3   From which material was the water-trough made?

A. Plastic   **C.** Stone

B. Glass   **D.** Tin

---

4   What colour bodies do venomous Sicilian snakes typically have?

A. Black   **C.** Green

B. Yellow   **D.** Silver

---

5   From where did the snake first appear before arriving at the water-trough?

A. It slid down through a small crack in a wall.

B. It slithered out from behind a tree.

C. It threw itself across the garden and onto the patio.

D. It was coiled up next to the trough and suddenly sprang up when the author first approached the trough.

/5

Answers

Extended answers with useful explanations are available online at
www.scholastic.co.uk/pass-your-11-plus/ extras or via the QR code.

1. The Tower of London
pp.5–9

1	B
2	C
3	C
4	B
5	A
6	D
7	B
8	D
9	A
10	B
11	A
12	D
13	C
14	B
15	C

2. Nellie Bly
pp.10–14

1	C
2	C
3	A
4	D
5	B
6	C
7	B
8	D
9	A
10	C
11	B
12	C
13	D
14	A
15	D

3. The Cotswolds
pp.15–19

1	B
2	D
3	A
4	B
5	D
6	B
7	C
8	A
9	C
10	C
11	C
12	A
13	D
14	B
15	B

4. Gibraltar
pp.20–24

1	C
2	C
3	D
4	B
5	D
6	A
7	D
8	D
9	B
10	C
11	B
12	C
13	B
14	A
15	D

5. The Museum of Liverpool
pp.25–29

1	D
2	B
3	A
4	C
5	D
6	C
7	D
8	B
9	C
10	C
11	A
12	B
13	D
14	C
15	A

6. The Great Plague and the Village of Eyam
pp.30–34

1	C
2	B
3	A
4	D
5	B
6	B
7	C
8	C
9	A
10	B
11	A
12	C
13	D
14	B
15	D

Answers

7. The Isles of Scilly
pp.35–39

1	A
2	C
3	B
4	C
5	C
6	B
7	C
8	B
9	D
10	D
11	C
12	A
13	A
14	D
15	D

8. Queen Mary 2 Cruise
pp.40–43

1	B
2	D
3	A
4	C
5	B
6	B
7	D
8	B
9	C
10	A

9. Autonomous Cars
pp.44–48

1	A
2	C
3	A
4	D
5	D
6	B
7	A
8	C
9	B
10	D
11	B
12	A
13	D
14	C
15	D

10. Prometheus the Fire-Giver
pp.49–51

1	D
2	A
3	B
4	C
5	B
6	A
7	D
8	C
9	D
10	A

11. The Pied Piper of Hamelin
pp.52–53

1	B
2	B
3	D
4	C
5	C

12. The Lake District
pp.54–56

1	B
2	B
3	C
4	A
5	D
6	C
7	D
8	A
9	B
10	D

13. My Father's War
pp.57–59

1	D
2	B
3	C
4	A
5	C
6	B
7	D
8	A
9	D
10	B

14. Snake
pp.60–61

1	D
2	B
3	C
4	B
5	A

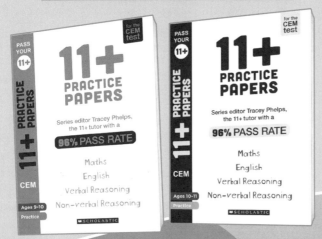